EGMONT
*We bring stories to life*

First published in Great Britain 2013 by Egmont UK Limited
The Yellow Building, 1 Nicholas Road, London W11 4AN

Text by Gemma Barder. Design by Martin Aggett

Thomas the Tank Engine & Friends™

CREATED BY BRITT ALLCROFT
Based on the Railway Series by the Reverend W Awdry
© 2013 Gullane (Thomas) LLC. A HIT Entertainment company.
Thomas the Tank Engine & Friends and Thomas & Friends are trademarks of Gullane (Thomas) Li
Thomas the Tank Engine & Friends and Design is Reg. U.S. Pat. & Tm. Off.

All rights reserved.

HiT entertainment

ISBN 978 1 4052 6585 0

# WELCOME TO SODOR!

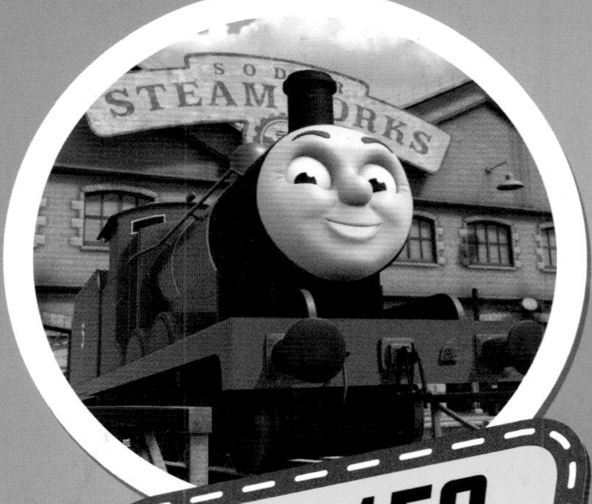

JAMES

PERCY

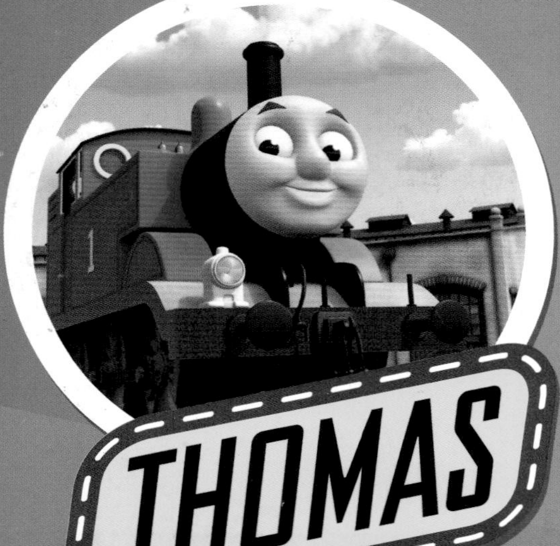

THOMAS

TOBY

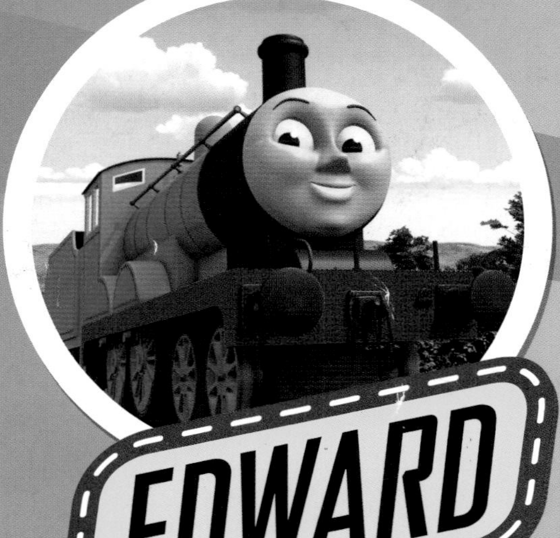

EDWARD

GORDON

HENRY

EMILY

**Find The Fat Controller!**

The Fat Controller is in every picture in this book. Can you see him?

There's **lots** to see and do on the Island of Sodor. Thomas and his friends are great at spotting things as they **chuff** along the tracks.

Now it's your turn to spot things, too! Take a look and see if you can **spot** each close-up in the big pictures.

**SEARCH AND FIND**

Can you be Really Useful and search out everything on the list, below?

# MAITHWAITE STATION

Harold and Thomas have arrived at Maithwaite station. What can you see?

Bertie

Green car

Station sign

Passengers

Thomas

Cows

Crates

Lamp post

Harold

The Fat Controller

# HAROLD'S HELIPAD

Keep clear! Harold's coming in to land! What can you find in this picture?

Butch

Thomas

Captain

Harold

Rocky

Workman

Rosie

Rescue Centre sign

Seagull

The Fat Controller

# FUN WITH PHOTOS!

Can you name the characters in the photographs?

# WHO'S WHO!

**Which engine is green and gold?**

**Which engines are the biggest?**

**Who is between Percy and James?**

**Which engine is made out of wood?**

**Which engine is red?**

**Which engine is closest to the photographer?**

Answers on page 24.

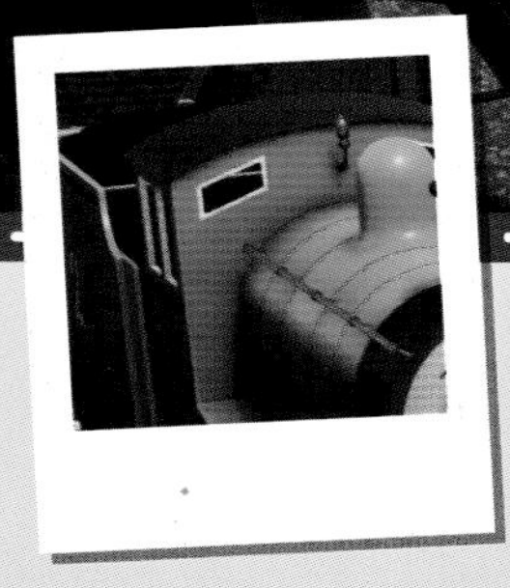

# THE SODOR STEAMWORKS

Lots of engines have gathered at the Steamworks. Who can you see?

Victor Percy Edward Emily The Fat Controller

# SEARCH AND FIND

Can you be Really Useful and search out everything on the list below?

Captain

Emily

Bertie and Butch

James

Rocky

Thomas Lots of passengers Toby Water tank The Fat Controller

# RECYCLING CENTRE

**The engines are busy dropping off rubbish to be recycled. Do you recycle?**

Whiff

Trucks

Chute

Crane

Chimney

# SORT THE RUBBISH!

**Where should each item of rubbish go?**

**Yoghurt pot**

**Tin can**

**Jam jar**

**Newspapers**

Answers on page 24.

Compactor

Tractor

Warehouse

Tin shed

The Fat Controller

# BRENDAM DOCKS

The engines have arrived at the Docks. What can you find in the picture?

Crane hook | James' dome | Spencer | Percy's 6 | Gordon

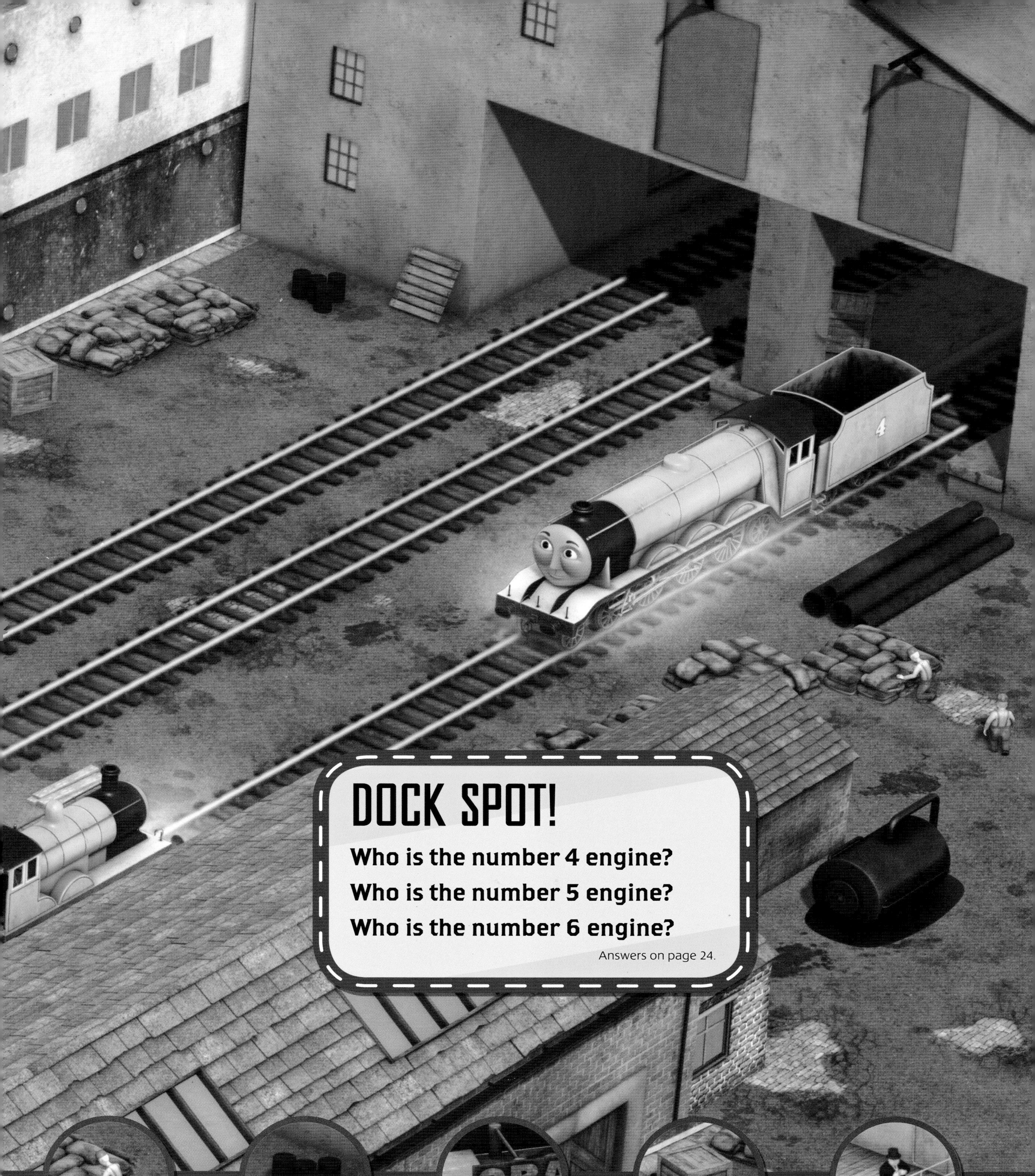


# DOCK SPOT!

**Who is the number 4 engine?**

**Who is the number 5 engine?**

**Who is the number 6 engine?**

Answers on page 24.

Workman

Oil drums

Cranky

Crate

The Fat Controller

# ANIMAL PARK COUNT

**Thomas and Percy are at the Animal Park! Can you count all the items on the list?**

- 1 Fat Controller
- 2 rabbits
- 3 giraffes
- 4 elephants
- 5 camels

6 lamp posts

7 picnic tables

8 zebras

9 children

10 birds

# BLUE MOUNTAIN QUARRY

Thomas is keeping himself busy at the Quarry! How many times does he appear?

Answer on page 24.

Merrick

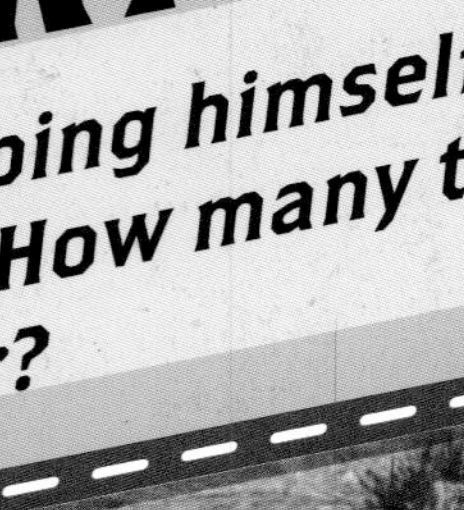

Sir Handel

Rheneas

Bridge

Victor

Funicular Railway Owen Toby Peter Sam The Fat Controller

# THOMAS AND HIS FRIENDS!

**Thomas has lots of friends on the Island of Sodor! How many of them do you know?**

# CHARACTER SPOT

The Fat Controller

Small girl

Lady Hatt

Workman

The Thin Controller

Duke and Duchess of Boxford

Mr Bubbles

Engineer

The Milkman

Giraffe

# WHAT ELSE?

There's lots more to find in this book. Can you spot these pictures?

# ANSWERS

## PAGES 8–9

Emily
Gordon and Henry
Thomas
Toby
James
Henry

## PAGES 14–15

The pot is plastic.
The tin can is metal.
The jam jar is glass.
The newspapers are paper.

## PAGES 16–17

The number 4 engine is Gordon.
The number 5 engine is James.
The number 6 engine is Percy.

## PAGES 20–21

Thomas appears 10 times.

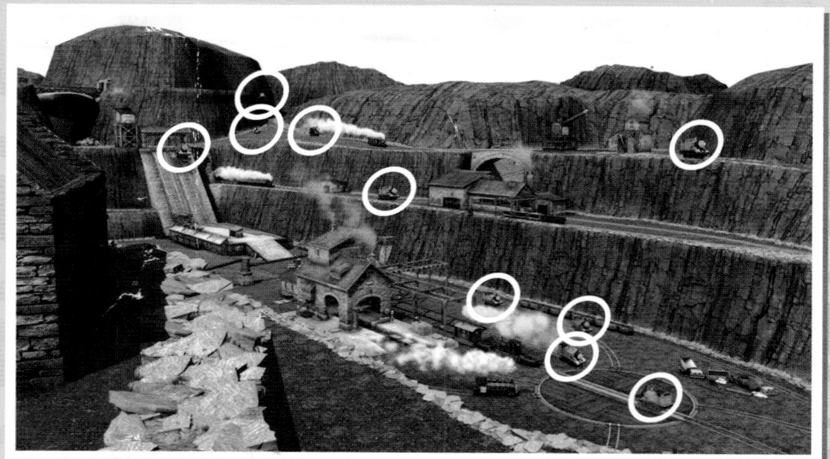